Dean is sixteen. He's just started college. He's making lots of new mates and is trying to fit in.

His friends have arranged to meet up in town on Friday evening.

"Are you coming, Dean?" Darren asks.

"I don't know. I'll ask my mum," Dean says.

Dean asks his mum but she says no.
"I don't want you staying out late. It's not nice in town on a Friday night," Mum says.

"Everyone's going. It's not fair.

I'm not going to have any friends," Dean grumbles.
He storms out of the kitchen and slams the door.

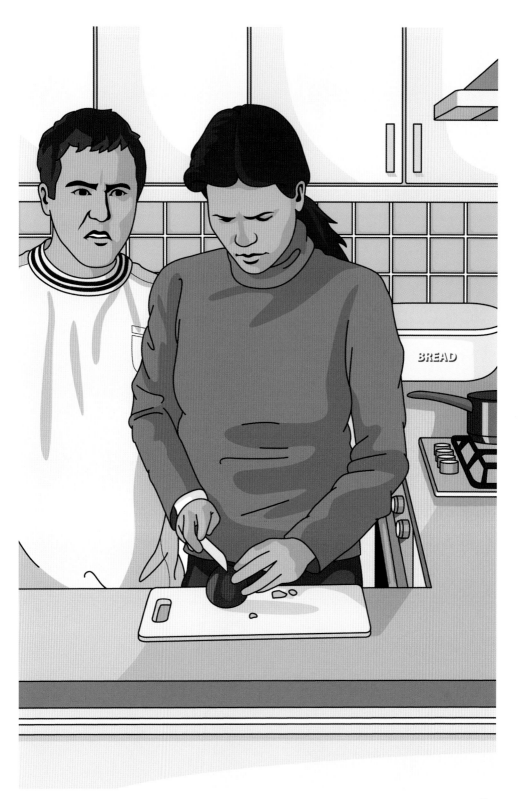

Dean's mum thinks it over.

"You can stay out until nine o'clock," she says.

"Nine o'clock? That's way too early. They'll think I'm a baby!" Dean says.

"Half past nine then. But no later," says Mum.

It's Friday evening. Dean gets changed.
He's pleased he can go, but he's
annoyed too.
Half past nine is too early to go home.
He wonders what his new friends will think.
Why does his mum treat him like a kid?

9

"I'll leave before she makes me put my coat on," Dean thinks. "None of my mates wear coats, even if it's cold."

At half past nine Dean looks at his watch.

"Don't go!" say his friends.

"Hang about with us. Your mum won't mind."

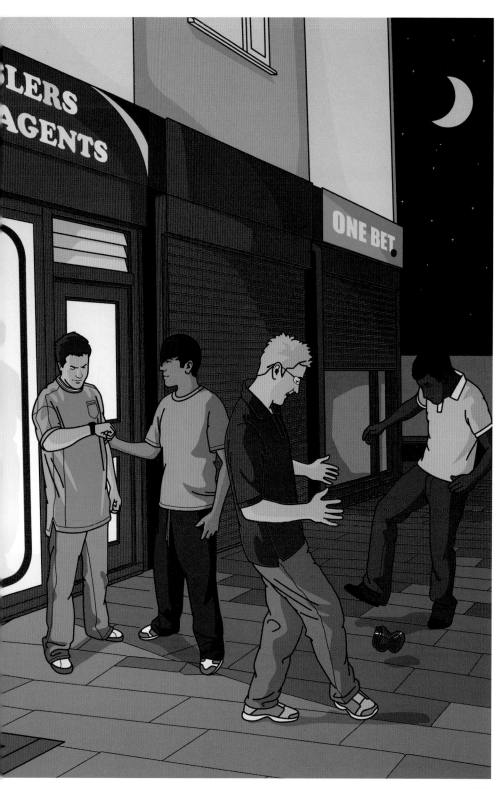

Dean knows she will mind. But he decides to stay out anyway.

"I'm an adult now. I can do what I like. I'm old enough to make my own decisions.

And I'm having a good time," he thinks.

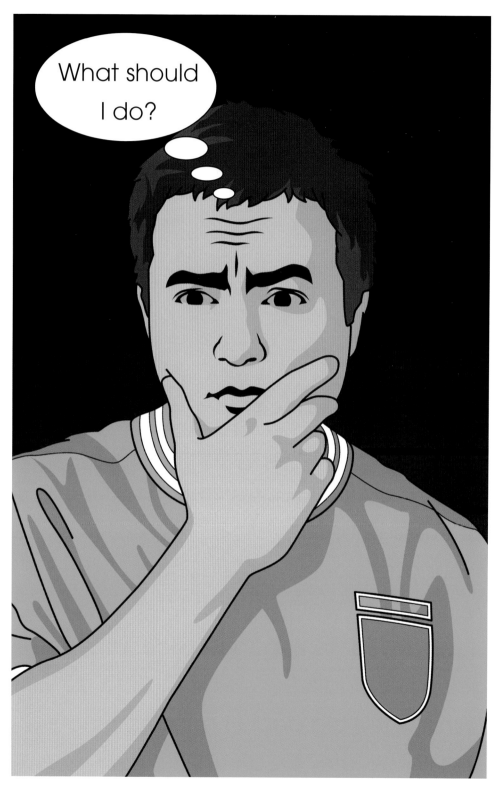

Dean gets home at eleven o'clock.
He's freezing cold and tired. His mum is
furious and upset.

"Your dad's been out looking for you.
We've been worried sick!" Mum says.

"I was about to ring the police. You're not
going out again."

"What's the big deal? I'm only an hour
and a half late." Dean says.